M000286526

M.C. ESCHER®
ADDRESS BOOK

Pomegranate

SAN FRANCISCO

Published by Pomegranate Communications, Inc.
Box 808022, Petaluma, CA 94975
800-227-1428; www.pomegranate.com

© 1988, 2003. All M. C. Escher's works © Cordon Art B.V., Baarn, the Netherlands.
All rights reserved. M. C. Escher® is a registered trademark of Cordon Art B.V.

ISBN 0-87654-120-1
Catalog No. A517

Pomegranate Europe Ltd.
Unit 1, Heathcote Business Centre, Hurlbutt Road
Warwick, Warwickshire CV34 6TD, U.K.

No part of this book may be reproduced or transmitted in any form or by any means,
electronic or mechanical, including photocopying, recording, or by any
information storage and retrieval system, without permission in
writing from the copyright holders.

Cover designed by Ronni Madrid
Printed in Korea

03 04 05 06 07 08 09 10 11   5 6 7 8 9 10 11 12 13

Maurits Cornelis Escher married Jetta Umiker in June, 1924, in Viareggio. In 1925 they moved to Rome into a small apartment on the Monte Verde.

There I was born in July, 1926. Immediately afterward we moved to a more spacious dwelling on the third floor of Via Allesandro Poerio 122, which remained my home during the first nine years of my life.

Today the house is still there. In those days over fifty years ago it stood isolated, and where now apartment buildings have risen there was an unkempt field, full of rough grasses and thistles, with a low shack inhabited by a poor family. We woke up in the early mornings from the crowing of their rooster or from the loud braying of their donkey, tethered to a stake in the middle of the field.

The apartment consisted of a long narrow entrance hall, a living and dining room with a small balcony overlooking the city, three bedrooms, a kitchen and a bathroom. The floors in the hall and the dining room were covered with ceramic tiles which Father had designed with a pattern of colored lines on a white background. The lines ran from one tile to the next, so that each line could be followed as it zigzagged from one end of the hall to the other. The tiles had not been properly laid and most of them had worked loose, so that they tipped slightly when you walked on them. For the children it was good fun to race through the house on a tricycle, as the tiles would rattle in a very satisfying way—less appreciated by the people living below.

(I remember) the Sunday walks, a regular ritual when (Father) would take my brother, Arthur, and me on an exploration of some part of Rome. (But) if the Sunday was too rainy to go out, Father spent his time with us in some other way, with games of his own invention. Our favorite ones were mazes and the "ball track."

A maze consisted of a long dark convoluted tunnel, as long as possible, through which we, the children, could move easily on hands and knees, but he could crawl only with difficulty. To build one, the furniture in the dining room was rearranged, chairs were tipped over, and all kinds of partitions built using easily available materials. The nursery table, the kitchen table, drawing boards and tea trays were used to create walls, with blankets and rugs to cover them, including the Persian carpet which was taken up for the occasion. Then came the fun of crawling fearfully through the dim tunnel, hearing the others scrambling about nearby . . . Undoubtedly my father enjoyed our fun, but remembering my experience with my own children, I think he must have derived a great deal of his pleasure from designing and building an improvised structure using the materials available at that moment.

The other favorite game was building a "ball track." The earliest models were primitive: Father joined the rails of our toy train together, raised one end of the track on a few toy building blocks and placed a wooden ball on its highest point. The ball would roll along the track until it fell off its end, clattering over the tiled floor. These small beginnings developed in later years into quite fantastic constructions. The basic principle was always the same: a hard ball was started to roll at the high point and would be made to descend to the floor by way of the longest, slowest and most varied route possible.

Father's studio upstairs was an adult place where children were tolerated on special occasions only and good behavior was expected. Its main features are visible in the 1935 lithograph *Hand with Reflecting Sphere*. Between the windows stood the large work table, on which the woodcutting implements or the lithographic stone would be laid out. In the early days I would stand there with my chin just above the tabletop—later I would be seated across from Father with paper and pencil to keep me busy, and I would watch in fascination as he worked away at a woodcut or lithograph.

During the creative period of studies for a new print he demanded solitude and quiet and could be quite irritated if disturbed. After such days or weeks of concentrated, solitary work we sensed a sudden release of tension, and the studio became accessible again. Then he would switch to the more relaxed activity of executing his drawings on wood or stone and allow us to look on.

It is not surprising that Father's hands are the feature of him which I most vividly remember. Looking at their precise movements, neatly arranging tools, sharpening gouges and chisels with rhythmic motions, preparing the wood to a smooth velvety finish, I could sense the pleasure that this activity gave him.

In 1943 Father made a self-portrait looking in a round mirror. It is very detailed and life-like and depicts him as he saw himself. The portrait has a flaw. Because it is drawn and "scraped" on parchment and is therefore not reversed by a printing process, it shows Father's asymmetric face with his nose tilted to his right. In reality, of course, his nose was tilted to the left, and I find that oddity disturbing.

For me, his 1948 lithograph "Drawing Hands" is, in a way, a truer self-portrait. These hands remind me, more strongly than any other of his works, of the person who was my father.

—excerpted from *Roman Memories* by George Escher,
published in the catalog of the Instituto Olandese di Roma's exhibition of 1985

June 17, 1898: Maurits Cornelis Escher (nicknamed "Mauk") is born in Leeuwarden, Holland. Spends most of his youth in Arnhem, and in lessons from F. W. van der Haager learns the rudiments of drawing and linoleum block printing. Indulges himself in films and reads Dostoevsky and Tolstoy.

1919: On his father's advice, Escher goes to Haarlem to study architecture at the now-defunct School of Architectural and Decorative Arts. Escher soon gives up architecture to study graphic arts under S. Jessurun de Mesquita.

1922: Travels to Italy and Spain.

1923: First solo exhibition in Siena, Italy. Moves to Rome.

1924: Marries Jetta Umiker, the daughter of a wealthy trader in Switzerland. Their first son, George, is born in 1926. Escher journeys each spring through the Italian countryside.

1935: The rise of fascism makes Rome less and less bearable. Escher moves with his family to Jetta's family home in Switzerland.

1936: Travels by ocean freighter along the coasts of Italy and France to Spain, where he makes detailed copies of the Moorish mosaics in the Alhambra and in the mosque at Cordoba. These mosaics greatly influence the direction of his art, turning it from landscapes to mental imagery.

1937: Moves to Ukkel, near Brussels, and from there to Baarn, Holland, in 1941; Escher lives there until 1970.

1940s–1950s: Through the 1940s, Escher's art is largely ignored. But in the 1950s he begins to gather recognition, first among scientists and mathematicians. Roger Penrose, Professor of Mathematics at Oxford University, publishes *Spacial Tribar*.

1951: *Time* and *Life* magazines publish articles on Escher.

1954: Large solo exhibition at Amsterdam's Stedelijk Museum on the occasion of the International Mathematical Conference. Exhibits also at the Whyte Gallery in Washington, D.C.

1959: *The Graphic Work of M. C. Escher* is published.

1960s: As soon as Escher's work is introduced in America, it finds tremendous support among the young generation. Articles about him appear in *The Saturday Evening Post* and *Scientific American*.

1968: Exhibits at the Mickelson Gallery in Washington, D.C., and at the Gemeenemuseum in The Hague.

1970: Moves to Lauren, Holland.

1971: Jetta separates from her husband and moves back to Switzerland. *The World of M. C. Escher* is published.

1972: M. C. Escher dies of cancer in a hospital in Hilversum.

Symmetry Watercolor 70
11 x 11 in., 1948

Symmetry Watercolor 78
7⅞ x 7⅞ in., 1950

NAME

ADDRESS

EMAIL

PHONE (H)

PHONE (W)

FAX

CELL/PAGER

NAME

ADDRESS

EMAIL

PHONE (H)

PHONE (W)

FAX

CELL/PAGER

NAME

ADDRESS

EMAIL

PHONE (H)

PHONE (W)

FAX

CELL/PAGER

NAME

ADDRESS

EMAIL

PHONE (H)

PHONE (W)

FAX

CELL/PAGER

NAME

ADDRESS

EMAIL

PHONE (H)

PHONE (W)

FAX

CELL/PAGER

NAME

ADDRESS

EMAIL

PHONE (H)

PHONE (W)

FAX

CELL/PAGER

NAME	PHONE (H)
ADDRESS	PHONE (W)
	FAX
EMAIL	CELL/PAGER

NAME	PHONE (H)
ADDRESS	PHONE (W)
	FAX
EMAIL	CELL/PAGER

NAME	PHONE (H)
ADDRESS	PHONE (W)
	FAX
EMAIL	CELL/PAGER

NAME	PHONE (H)
ADDRESS	PHONE (W)
	FAX
EMAIL	CELL/PAGER

NAME	PHONE (H)
ADDRESS	PHONE (W)
	FAX
EMAIL	CELL/PAGER

NAME	PHONE (H)
ADDRESS	PHONE (W)
	FAX
EMAIL	CELL/PAGER

NAME

ADDRESS

EMAIL

PHONE (H)

PHONE (W)

FAX

CELL/PAGER

NAME

ADDRESS

EMAIL

PHONE (H)

PHONE (W)

FAX

CELL/PAGER

NAME

ADDRESS

EMAIL

PHONE (H)

PHONE (W)

FAX

CELL/PAGER

NAME

ADDRESS

EMAIL

PHONE (H)

PHONE (W)

FAX

CELL/PAGER

NAME

ADDRESS

EMAIL

PHONE (H)

PHONE (W)

FAX

CELL/PAGER

NAME

ADDRESS

EMAIL

PHONE (H)

PHONE (W)

FAX

CELL/PAGER

NAME	PHONE (H)
ADDRESS	PHONE (W)
	FAX
EMAIL	CELL/PAGER

NAME	PHONE (H)
ADDRESS	PHONE (W)
	FAX
EMAIL	CELL/PAGER

NAME	PHONE (H)
ADDRESS	PHONE (W)
	FAX
EMAIL	CELL/PAGER

NAME	PHONE (H)
ADDRESS	PHONE (W)
	FAX
EMAIL	CELL/PAGER

NAME	PHONE (H)
ADDRESS	PHONE (W)
	FAX
EMAIL	CELL/PAGER

NAME	PHONE (H)
ADDRESS	PHONE (W)
	FAX
EMAIL	CELL/PAGER

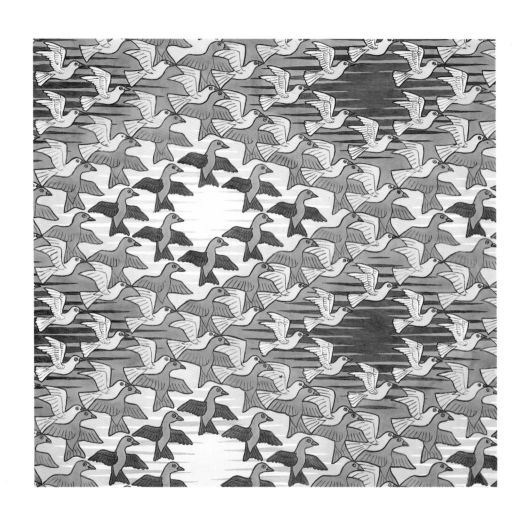

Birds in Space

Watercolor, 27½ x 27½ in.

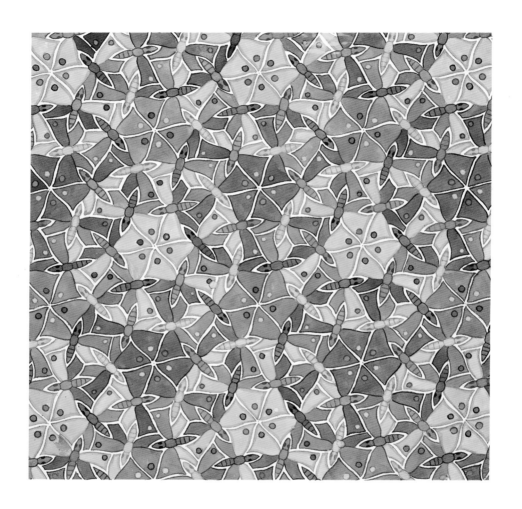

Symmetry Watercolor 79
11 x 11 in., 1950

NAME	PHONE (H)
ADDRESS	PHONE (W)
	FAX
EMAIL	CELL/PAGER

NAME	PHONE (H)
ADDRESS	PHONE (W)
	FAX
EMAIL	CELL/PAGER

NAME	PHONE (H)
ADDRESS	PHONE (W)
	FAX
EMAIL	CELL/PAGER

NAME	PHONE (H)
ADDRESS	PHONE (W)
	FAX
EMAIL	CELL/PAGER

NAME	PHONE (H)
ADDRESS	PHONE (W)
	FAX
EMAIL	CELL/PAGER

NAME	PHONE (H)
ADDRESS	PHONE (W)
	FAX
EMAIL	CELL/PAGER

NAME

ADDRESS

EMAIL

PHONE (H)

PHONE (W)

FAX

CELL/PAGER

NAME

ADDRESS

EMAIL

PHONE (H)

PHONE (W)

FAX

CELL/PAGER

NAME

ADDRESS

EMAIL

PHONE (H)

PHONE (W)

FAX

CELL/PAGER

NAME

ADDRESS

EMAIL

PHONE (H)

PHONE (W)

FAX

CELL/PAGER

NAME

ADDRESS

EMAIL

PHONE (H)

PHONE (W)

FAX

CELL/PAGER

NAME

ADDRESS

EMAIL

PHONE (H)

PHONE (W)

FAX

CELL/PAGER

NAME

ADDRESS

EMAIL

PHONE (H)

PHONE (W)

FAX

CELL/PAGER

NAME

ADDRESS

EMAIL

PHONE (H)

PHONE (W)

FAX

CELL/PAGER

NAME

ADDRESS

EMAIL

PHONE (H)

PHONE (W)

FAX

CELL/PAGER

NAME

ADDRESS

EMAIL

PHONE (H)

PHONE (W)

FAX

CELL/PAGER

NAME

ADDRESS

EMAIL

PHONE (H)

PHONE (W)

FAX

CELL/PAGER

NAME

ADDRESS

EMAIL

PHONE (H)

PHONE (W)

FAX

CELL/PAGER

NAME

ADDRESS

EMAIL

PHONE (H)

PHONE (W)

FAX

CELL/PAGER

NAME

ADDRESS

EMAIL

PHONE (H)

PHONE (W)

FAX

CELL/PAGER

NAME

ADDRESS

EMAIL

PHONE (H)

PHONE (W)

FAX

CELL/PAGER

NAME

ADDRESS

EMAIL

PHONE (H)

PHONE (W)

FAX

CELL/PAGER

NAME

ADDRESS

EMAIL

PHONE (H)

PHONE (W)

FAX

CELL/PAGER

NAME

ADDRESS

EMAIL

PHONE (H)

PHONE (W)

FAX

CELL/PAGER

Three Worlds
Lithograph, 14¼ x 9¾ in., 1955

Still Life with Mirror

Lithograph, 15½ x 11¼ in., 1934

NAME	PHONE (H)
ADDRESS	PHONE (W)
	FAX
EMAIL	CELL/PAGER

NAME	PHONE (H)
ADDRESS	PHONE (W)
	FAX
EMAIL	CELL/PAGER

NAME	PHONE (H)
ADDRESS	PHONE (W)
	FAX
EMAIL	CELL/PAGER

NAME	PHONE (H)
ADDRESS	PHONE (W)
	FAX
EMAIL	CELL/PAGER

NAME	PHONE (H)
ADDRESS	PHONE (W)
	FAX
EMAIL	CELL/PAGER

NAME	PHONE (H)
ADDRESS	PHONE (W)
	FAX
EMAIL	CELL/PAGER

NAME

ADDRESS

EMAIL

PHONE (H)

PHONE (W)

FAX

CELL/PAGER

NAME

ADDRESS

EMAIL

PHONE (H)

PHONE (W)

FAX

CELL/PAGER

NAME

ADDRESS

EMAIL

PHONE (H)

PHONE (W)

FAX

CELL/PAGER

NAME

ADDRESS

EMAIL

PHONE (H)

PHONE (W)

FAX

CELL/PAGER

NAME

ADDRESS

EMAIL

PHONE (H)

PHONE (W)

FAX

CELL/PAGER

NAME

ADDRESS

EMAIL

PHONE (H)

PHONE (W)

FAX

CELL/PAGER

NAME

ADDRESS

EMAIL

PHONE (H)

PHONE (W)

FAX

CELL/PAGER

NAME

ADDRESS

EMAIL

PHONE (H)

PHONE (W)

FAX

CELL/PAGER

NAME

ADDRESS

EMAIL

PHONE (H)

PHONE (W)

FAX

CELL/PAGER

NAME

ADDRESS

EMAIL

PHONE (H)

PHONE (W)

FAX

CELL/PAGER

NAME

ADDRESS

EMAIL

PHONE (H)

PHONE (W)

FAX

CELL/PAGER

NAME

ADDRESS

EMAIL

PHONE (H)

PHONE (W)

FAX

CELL/PAGER

NAME	PHONE (H)
ADDRESS	PHONE (W)
	FAX
EMAIL	CELL/PAGER

NAME	PHONE (H)
ADDRESS	PHONE (W)
	FAX
EMAIL	CELL/PAGER

NAME	PHONE (H)
ADDRESS	PHONE (W)
	FAX
EMAIL	CELL/PAGER

NAME	PHONE (H)
ADDRESS	PHONE (W)
	FAX
EMAIL	CELL/PAGER

NAME	PHONE (H)
ADDRESS	PHONE (W)
	FAX
EMAIL	CELL/PAGER

NAME	PHONE (H)
ADDRESS	PHONE (W)
	FAX
EMAIL	CELL/PAGER

Depth
Wood engraving and woodcut, 12⅝ x 9 in., 1955

Symmetry Watercolor 117

9¼ x 9¼ in., 1963

NAME	PHONE (H)
ADDRESS	PHONE (W)
	FAX
EMAIL	CELL/PAGER

NAME	PHONE (H)
ADDRESS	PHONE (W)
	FAX
EMAIL	CELL/PAGER

NAME	PHONE (H)
ADDRESS	PHONE (W)
	FAX
EMAIL	CELL/PAGER

NAME	PHONE (H)
ADDRESS	PHONE (W)
	FAX
EMAIL	CELL/PAGER

NAME	PHONE (H)
ADDRESS	PHONE (W)
	FAX
EMAIL	CELL/PAGER

NAME	PHONE (H)
ADDRESS	PHONE (W)
	FAX
EMAIL	CELL/PAGER

NAME	PHONE (H)
ADDRESS	PHONE (W)
	FAX
EMAIL	CELL/PAGER

NAME	PHONE (H)
ADDRESS	PHONE (W)
	FAX
EMAIL	CELL/PAGER

NAME	PHONE (H)
ADDRESS	PHONE (W)
	FAX
EMAIL	CELL/PAGER

NAME	PHONE (H)
ADDRESS	PHONE (W)
	FAX
EMAIL	CELL/PAGER

NAME	PHONE (H)
ADDRESS	PHONE (W)
	FAX
EMAIL	CELL/PAGER

NAME	PHONE (H)
ADDRESS	PHONE (W)
	FAX
EMAIL	CELL/PAGER

NAME	PHONE (H)
ADDRESS	PHONE (W)
	FAX
EMAIL	CELL/PAGER

NAME	PHONE (H)
ADDRESS	PHONE (W)
	FAX
EMAIL	CELL/PAGER

NAME	PHONE (H)
ADDRESS	PHONE (W)
	FAX
EMAIL	CELL/PAGER

NAME	PHONE (H)
ADDRESS	PHONE (W)
	FAX
EMAIL	CELL/PAGER

NAME	PHONE (H)
ADDRESS	PHONE (W)
	FAX
EMAIL	CELL/PAGER

NAME	PHONE (H)
ADDRESS	PHONE (W)
	FAX
EMAIL	CELL/PAGER

NAME

ADDRESS

EMAIL

PHONE (H)

PHONE (W)

FAX

CELL/PAGER

NAME

ADDRESS

EMAIL

PHONE (H)

PHONE (W)

FAX

CELL/PAGER

NAME

ADDRESS

EMAIL

PHONE (H)

PHONE (W)

FAX

CELL/PAGER

NAME

ADDRESS

EMAIL

PHONE (H)

PHONE (W)

FAX

CELL/PAGER

NAME

ADDRESS

EMAIL

PHONE (H)

PHONE (W)

FAX

CELL/PAGER

NAME

ADDRESS

EMAIL

PHONE (H)

PHONE (W)

FAX

CELL/PAGER

Belvedere
Lithograph, 18⅜ x 11⅝ in., 1958

Snow

Lithograph, 12¾ x 10¾ in., 1936

NAME

ADDRESS

EMAIL

PHONE (H)

PHONE (W)

FAX

CELL/PAGER

NAME

ADDRESS

EMAIL

PHONE (H)

PHONE (W)

FAX

CELL/PAGER

NAME

ADDRESS

EMAIL

PHONE (H)

PHONE (W)

FAX

CELL/PAGER

NAME

ADDRESS

EMAIL

PHONE (H)

PHONE (W)

FAX

CELL/PAGER

NAME

ADDRESS

EMAIL

PHONE (H)

PHONE (W)

FAX

CELL/PAGER

NAME

ADDRESS

EMAIL

PHONE (H)

PHONE (W)

FAX

CELL/PAGER

NAME

ADDRESS

EMAIL

PHONE (H)

PHONE (W)

FAX

CELL/PAGER

NAME

ADDRESS

EMAIL

PHONE (H)

PHONE (W)

FAX

CELL/PAGER

NAME

ADDRESS

EMAIL

PHONE (H)

PHONE (W)

FAX

CELL/PAGER

NAME

ADDRESS

EMAIL

PHONE (H)

PHONE (W)

FAX

CELL/PAGER

NAME

ADDRESS

EMAIL

PHONE (H)

PHONE (W)

FAX

CELL/PAGER

NAME

ADDRESS

EMAIL

PHONE (H)

PHONE (W)

FAX

CELL/PAGER

NAME

ADDRESS

EMAIL

PHONE (H)

PHONE (W)

FAX

CELL/PAGER

NAME

ADDRESS

EMAIL

PHONE (H)

PHONE (W)

FAX

CELL/PAGER

NAME

ADDRESS

EMAIL

PHONE (H)

PHONE (W)

FAX

CELL/PAGER

NAME

ADDRESS

EMAIL

PHONE (H)

PHONE (W)

FAX

CELL/PAGER

NAME

ADDRESS

EMAIL

PHONE (H)

PHONE (W)

FAX

CELL/PAGER

NAME

ADDRESS

EMAIL

PHONE (H)

PHONE (W)

FAX

CELL/PAGER

NAME

ADDRESS

EMAIL

PHONE (H)

PHONE (W)

FAX

CELL/PAGER

NAME

ADDRESS

EMAIL

PHONE (H)

PHONE (W)

FAX

CELL/PAGER

NAME

ADDRESS

EMAIL

PHONE (H)

PHONE (W)

FAX

CELL/PAGER

NAME

ADDRESS

EMAIL

PHONE (H)

PHONE (W)

FAX

CELL/PAGER

NAME

ADDRESS

EMAIL

PHONE (H)

PHONE (W)

FAX

CELL/PAGER

NAME

ADDRESS

EMAIL

PHONE (H)

PHONE (W)

FAX

CELL/PAGER

Relativity
Lithograph, 10⅞ x 11½ in., 1953

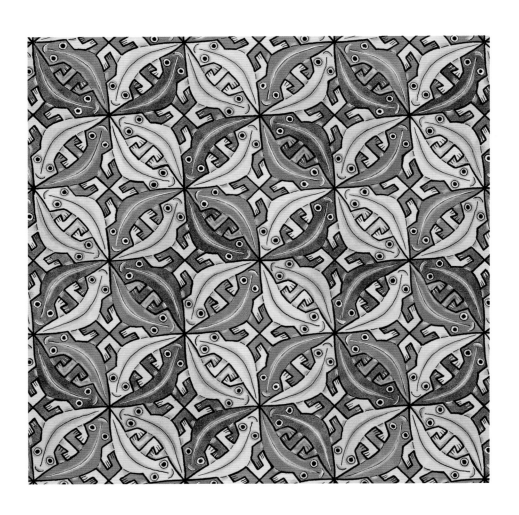

Symmetry Watercolor 118

$9^{11}/_{16}$ x $9^{11}/_{16}$ in., 1963

NAME	PHONE (H)
ADDRESS	PHONE (W)
	FAX
EMAIL	CELL/PAGER

NAME	PHONE (H)
ADDRESS	PHONE (W)
	FAX
EMAIL	CELL/PAGER

NAME	PHONE (H)
ADDRESS	PHONE (W)
	FAX
EMAIL	CELL/PAGER

NAME	PHONE (H)
ADDRESS	PHONE (W)
	FAX
EMAIL	CELL/PAGER

NAME	PHONE (H)
ADDRESS	PHONE (W)
	FAX
EMAIL	CELL/PAGER

NAME	PHONE (H)
ADDRESS	PHONE (W)
	FAX
EMAIL	CELL/PAGER

NAME

ADDRESS

EMAIL

PHONE (H)

PHONE (W)

FAX

CELL/PAGER

NAME

ADDRESS

EMAIL

PHONE (H)

PHONE (W)

FAX

CELL/PAGER

NAME

ADDRESS

EMAIL

PHONE (H)

PHONE (W)

FAX

CELL/PAGER

NAME

ADDRESS

EMAIL

PHONE (H)

PHONE (W)

FAX

CELL/PAGER

NAME

ADDRESS

EMAIL

PHONE (H)

PHONE (W)

FAX

CELL/PAGER

NAME

ADDRESS

EMAIL

PHONE (H)

PHONE (W)

FAX

CELL/PAGER

NAME

ADDRESS

EMAIL

PHONE (H)

PHONE (W)

FAX

CELL/PAGER

NAME

ADDRESS

EMAIL

PHONE (H)

PHONE (W)

FAX

CELL/PAGER

NAME

ADDRESS

EMAIL

PHONE (H)

PHONE (W)

FAX

CELL/PAGER

NAME

ADDRESS

EMAIL

PHONE (H)

PHONE (W)

FAX

CELL/PAGER

NAME

ADDRESS

EMAIL

PHONE (H)

PHONE (W)

FAX

CELL/PAGER

NAME

ADDRESS

EMAIL

PHONE (H)

PHONE (W)

FAX

CELL/PAGER

NAME

ADDRESS

EMAIL

PHONE (H)

PHONE (W)

FAX

CELL/PAGER

NAME

ADDRESS

EMAIL

PHONE (H)

PHONE (W)

FAX

CELL/PAGER

NAME

ADDRESS

EMAIL

PHONE (H)

PHONE (W)

FAX

CELL/PAGER

NAME

ADDRESS

EMAIL

PHONE (H)

PHONE (W)

FAX

CELL/PAGER

NAME

ADDRESS

EMAIL

PHONE (H)

PHONE (W)

FAX

CELL/PAGER

NAME

ADDRESS

EMAIL

PHONE (H)

PHONE (W)

FAX

CELL/PAGER

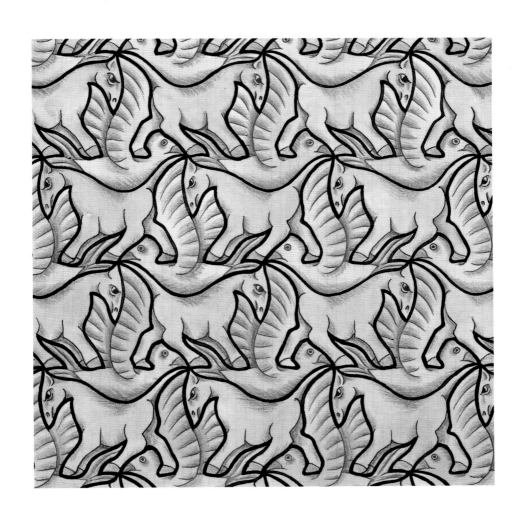

Symmetry Watercolor 76
8 x 8 in., 1949

Symmetry Drawing 72
10½ x 7⅞ in., 1948

NAME

ADDRESS

EMAIL

PHONE (H)

PHONE (W)

FAX

CELL/PAGER

NAME

ADDRESS

EMAIL

PHONE (H)

PHONE (W)

FAX

CELL/PAGER

NAME

ADDRESS

EMAIL

PHONE (H)

PHONE (W)

FAX

CELL/PAGER

NAME

ADDRESS

EMAIL

PHONE (H)

PHONE (W)

FAX

CELL/PAGER

NAME

ADDRESS

EMAIL

PHONE (H)

PHONE (W)

FAX

CELL/PAGER

NAME

ADDRESS

EMAIL

PHONE (H)

PHONE (W)

FAX

CELL/PAGER

NAME	PHONE (H)
ADDRESS	PHONE (W)
	FAX
EMAIL	CELL/PAGER

NAME	PHONE (H)
ADDRESS	PHONE (W)
	FAX
EMAIL	CELL/PAGER

NAME	PHONE (H)
ADDRESS	PHONE (W)
	FAX
EMAIL	CELL/PAGER

NAME	PHONE (H)
ADDRESS	PHONE (W)
	FAX
EMAIL	CELL/PAGER

NAME	PHONE (H)
ADDRESS	PHONE (W)
	FAX
EMAIL	CELL/PAGER

NAME	PHONE (H)
ADDRESS	PHONE (W)
	FAX
EMAIL	CELL/PAGER

NAME	PHONE (H)
ADDRESS	PHONE (W)
	FAX
EMAIL	CELL/PAGER

NAME	PHONE (H)
ADDRESS	PHONE (W)
	FAX
EMAIL	CELL/PAGER

NAME	PHONE (H)
ADDRESS	PHONE (W)
	FAX
EMAIL	CELL/PAGER

NAME	PHONE (H)
ADDRESS	PHONE (W)
	FAX
EMAIL	CELL/PAGER

NAME	PHONE (H)
ADDRESS	PHONE (W)
	FAX
EMAIL	CELL/PAGER

NAME	PHONE (H)
ADDRESS	PHONE (W)
	FAX
EMAIL	CELL/PAGER

NAME

ADDRESS

EMAIL

PHONE (H)

PHONE (W)

FAX

CELL/PAGER

NAME

ADDRESS

EMAIL

PHONE (H)

PHONE (W)

FAX

CELL/PAGER

NAME

ADDRESS

EMAIL

PHONE (H)

PHONE (W)

FAX

CELL/PAGER

NAME

ADDRESS

EMAIL

PHONE (H)

PHONE (W)

FAX

CELL/PAGER

NAME

ADDRESS

EMAIL

PHONE (H)

PHONE (W)

FAX

CELL/PAGER

NAME

ADDRESS

EMAIL

PHONE (H)

PHONE (W)

FAX

CELL/PAGER

Rind
Color woodcut, 13½ x 9¼ in. 1955

Pebble

Ink on paper, 6⁵⁄₁₆ x 7¹³⁄₁₆ in., 1942

NAME

ADDRESS

EMAIL

PHONE (H)

PHONE (W)

FAX

CELL/PAGER

NAME

ADDRESS

EMAIL

PHONE (H)

PHONE (W)

FAX

CELL/PAGER

NAME

ADDRESS

EMAIL

PHONE (H)

PHONE (W)

FAX

CELL/PAGER

NAME

ADDRESS

EMAIL

PHONE (H)

PHONE (W)

FAX

CELL/PAGER

NAME

ADDRESS

EMAIL

PHONE (H)

PHONE (W)

FAX

CELL/PAGER

NAME

ADDRESS

EMAIL

PHONE (H)

PHONE (W)

FAX

CELL/PAGER

NAME	PHONE (H)
ADDRESS	PHONE (W)
	FAX
EMAIL	CELL/PAGER

NAME	PHONE (H)
ADDRESS	PHONE (W)
	FAX
EMAIL	CELL/PAGER

NAME	PHONE (H)
ADDRESS	PHONE (W)
	FAX
EMAIL	CELL/PAGER

NAME	PHONE (H)
ADDRESS	PHONE (W)
	FAX
EMAIL	CELL/PAGER

NAME	PHONE (H)
ADDRESS	PHONE (W)
	FAX
EMAIL	CELL/PAGER

NAME	PHONE (H)
ADDRESS	PHONE (W)
	FAX
EMAIL	CELL/PAGER

NAME

ADDRESS

EMAIL

PHONE (H)

PHONE (W)

FAX

CELL/PAGER

NAME

ADDRESS

EMAIL

PHONE (H)

PHONE (W)

FAX

CELL/PAGER

NAME

ADDRESS

EMAIL

PHONE (H)

PHONE (W)

FAX

CELL/PAGER

NAME

ADDRESS

EMAIL

PHONE (H)

PHONE (W)

FAX

CELL/PAGER

NAME

ADDRESS

EMAIL

PHONE (H)

PHONE (W)

FAX

CELL/PAGER

NAME

ADDRESS

EMAIL

PHONE (H)

PHONE (W)

FAX

CELL/PAGER

NAME	PHONE (H)
ADDRESS	PHONE (W)
	FAX
EMAIL	CELL/PAGER

NAME	PHONE (H)
ADDRESS	PHONE (W)
	FAX
EMAIL	CELL/PAGER

NAME	PHONE (H)
ADDRESS	PHONE (W)
	FAX
EMAIL	CELL/PAGER

NAME	PHONE (H)
ADDRESS	PHONE (W)
	FAX
EMAIL	CELL/PAGER

NAME	PHONE (H)
ADDRESS	PHONE (W)
	FAX
EMAIL	CELL/PAGER

NAME	PHONE (H)
ADDRESS	PHONE (W)
	FAX
EMAIL	CELL/PAGER

Symmetry Watercolor 115
7⅞ x 7⅞ in., 1963

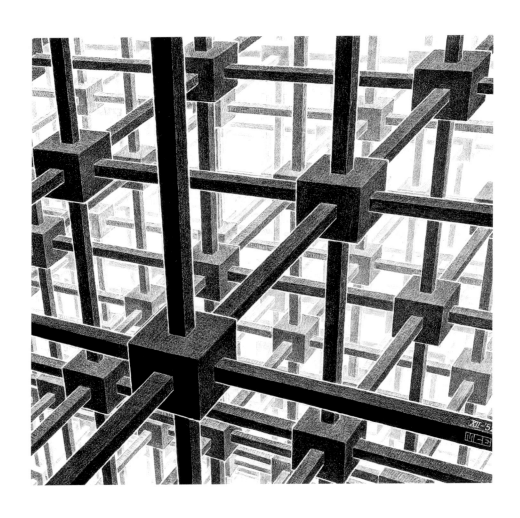

Cubic Space Division

Lithograph, 10½ x 10½ in., 1952

NAME

PHONE (H)

ADDRESS

PHONE (W)

FAX

EMAIL

CELL/PAGER

NAME

PHONE (H)

ADDRESS

PHONE (W)

FAX

EMAIL

CELL/PAGER

NAME

PHONE (H)

ADDRESS

PHONE (W)

FAX

EMAIL

CELL/PAGER

NAME

PHONE (H)

ADDRESS

PHONE (W)

FAX

EMAIL

CELL/PAGER

NAME

PHONE (H)

ADDRESS

PHONE (W)

FAX

EMAIL

CELL/PAGER

NAME

PHONE (H)

ADDRESS

PHONE (W)

FAX

EMAIL

CELL/PAGER

NAME

ADDRESS

EMAIL

PHONE (H)

PHONE (W)

FAX

CELL/PAGER

NAME

ADDRESS

EMAIL

PHONE (H)

PHONE (W)

FAX

CELL/PAGER

NAME

ADDRESS

EMAIL

PHONE (H)

PHONE (W)

FAX

CELL/PAGER

NAME

ADDRESS

EMAIL

PHONE (H)

PHONE (W)

FAX

CELL/PAGER

NAME

ADDRESS

EMAIL

PHONE (H)

PHONE (W)

FAX

CELL/PAGER

NAME

ADDRESS

EMAIL

PHONE (H)

PHONE (W)

FAX

CELL/PAGER

NAME

ADDRESS

EMAIL

PHONE (H)

PHONE (W)

FAX

CELL/PAGER

NAME

ADDRESS

EMAIL

PHONE (H)

PHONE (W)

FAX

CELL/PAGER

NAME

ADDRESS

EMAIL

PHONE (H)

PHONE (W)

FAX

CELL/PAGER

NAME

ADDRESS

EMAIL

PHONE (H)

PHONE (W)

FAX

CELL/PAGER

NAME

ADDRESS

EMAIL

PHONE (H)

PHONE (W)

FAX

CELL/PAGER

NAME

ADDRESS

EMAIL

PHONE (H)

PHONE (W)

FAX

CELL/PAGER

NAME	PHONE (H)
ADDRESS	PHONE (W)
	FAX
EMAIL	CELL/PAGER

NAME	PHONE (H)
ADDRESS	PHONE (W)
	FAX
EMAIL	CELL/PAGER

NAME	PHONE (H)
ADDRESS	PHONE (W)
	FAX
EMAIL	CELL/PAGER

NAME	PHONE (H)
ADDRESS	PHONE (W)
	FAX
EMAIL	CELL/PAGER

NAME	PHONE (H)
ADDRESS	PHONE (W)
	FAX
EMAIL	CELL/PAGER

NAME	PHONE (H)
ADDRESS	PHONE (W)
	FAX
EMAIL	CELL/PAGER

L

Hand with Reflecting Sphere
Lithograph, 12½ x 8⅜ in., 1935

L

Symmetry Watercolor 55

8 ¹¹⁄₁₆ x 8¹⁄₁₆ in., 1942

NAME		PHONE (H)
ADDRESS		PHONE (W)
		FAX
EMAIL		CELL/PAGER

NAME		PHONE (H)
ADDRESS		PHONE (W)
		FAX
EMAIL		CELL/PAGER

NAME		PHONE (H)
ADDRESS		PHONE (W)
		FAX
EMAIL		CELL/PAGER

NAME		PHONE (H)
ADDRESS		PHONE (W)
		FAX
EMAIL		CELL/PAGER

NAME		PHONE (H)
ADDRESS		PHONE (W)
		FAX
EMAIL		CELL/PAGER

NAME		PHONE (H)
ADDRESS		PHONE (W)
		FAX
EMAIL		CELL/PAGER

NAME

ADDRESS

EMAIL

PHONE (H)

PHONE (W)

FAX

CELL/PAGER

NAME

ADDRESS

EMAIL

PHONE (H)

PHONE (W)

FAX

CELL/PAGER

NAME

ADDRESS

EMAIL

PHONE (H)

PHONE (W)

FAX

CELL/PAGER

NAME

ADDRESS

EMAIL

PHONE (H)

PHONE (W)

FAX

CELL/PAGER

NAME

ADDRESS

EMAIL

PHONE (H)

PHONE (W)

FAX

CELL/PAGER

NAME

ADDRESS

EMAIL

PHONE (H)

PHONE (W)

FAX

CELL/PAGER

NAME

ADDRESS

EMAIL

PHONE (H)

PHONE (W)

FAX

CELL/PAGER

NAME

ADDRESS

EMAIL

PHONE (H)

PHONE (W)

FAX

CELL/PAGER

NAME

ADDRESS

EMAIL

PHONE (H)

PHONE (W)

FAX

CELL/PAGER

NAME

ADDRESS

EMAIL

PHONE (H)

PHONE (W)

FAX

CELL/PAGER

NAME

ADDRESS

EMAIL

PHONE (H)

PHONE (W)

FAX

CELL/PAGER

NAME

ADDRESS

EMAIL

PHONE (H)

PHONE (W)

FAX

CELL/PAGER

NAME

ADDRESS

EMAIL

PHONE (H)

PHONE (W)

FAX

CELL/PAGER

NAME

ADDRESS

EMAIL

PHONE (H)

PHONE (W)

FAX

CELL/PAGER

NAME

ADDRESS

EMAIL

PHONE (H)

PHONE (W)

FAX

CELL/PAGER

NAME

ADDRESS

EMAIL

PHONE (H)

PHONE (W)

FAX

CELL/PAGER

NAME

ADDRESS

EMAIL

PHONE (H)

PHONE (W)

FAX

CELL/PAGER

NAME

ADDRESS

EMAIL

PHONE (H)

PHONE (W)

FAX

CELL/PAGER

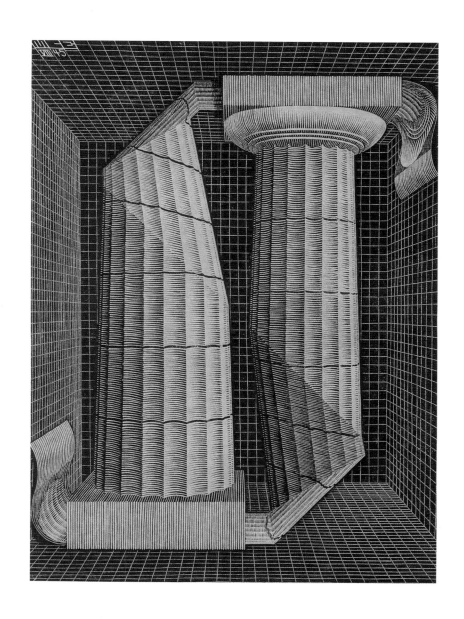

Doric Columns
Wood engraving, 12⅝ x 9½ in., 1945

Symmetry Watercolor 109 II
11½ x 6¼ in., 1961

NAME

ADDRESS

EMAIL

PHONE (H)

PHONE (W)

FAX

CELL/PAGER

NAME

ADDRESS

EMAIL

PHONE (H)

PHONE (W)

FAX

CELL/PAGER

NAME

ADDRESS

EMAIL

PHONE (H)

PHONE (W)

FAX

CELL/PAGER

NAME

ADDRESS

EMAIL

PHONE (H)

PHONE (W)

FAX

CELL/PAGER

NAME

ADDRESS

EMAIL

PHONE (H)

PHONE (W)

FAX

CELL/PAGER

NAME

ADDRESS

EMAIL

PHONE (H)

PHONE (W)

FAX

CELL/PAGER

NAME

ADDRESS

EMAIL

PHONE (H)

PHONE (W)

FAX

CELL/PAGER

NAME

ADDRESS

EMAIL

PHONE (H)

PHONE (W)

FAX

CELL/PAGER

NAME

ADDRESS

EMAIL

PHONE (H)

PHONE (W)

FAX

CELL/PAGER

NAME

ADDRESS

EMAIL

PHONE (H)

PHONE (W)

FAX

CELL/PAGER

NAME

ADDRESS

EMAIL

PHONE (H)

PHONE (W)

FAX

CELL/PAGER

NAME

ADDRESS

EMAIL

PHONE (H)

PHONE (W)

FAX

CELL/PAGER

NAME

ADDRESS

EMAIL

PHONE (H)

PHONE (W)

FAX

CELL/PAGER

NAME

ADDRESS

EMAIL

PHONE (H)

PHONE (W)

FAX

CELL/PAGER

NAME

ADDRESS

EMAIL

PHONE (H)

PHONE (W)

FAX

CELL/PAGER

NAME

ADDRESS

EMAIL

PHONE (H)

PHONE (W)

FAX

CELL/PAGER

NAME

ADDRESS

EMAIL

PHONE (H)

PHONE (W)

FAX

CELL/PAGER

NAME

ADDRESS

EMAIL

PHONE (H)

PHONE (W)

FAX

CELL/PAGER

NAME

ADDRESS

EMAIL

PHONE (H)

PHONE (W)

FAX

CELL/PAGER

NAME

ADDRESS

EMAIL

PHONE (H)

PHONE (W)

FAX

CELL/PAGER

NAME

ADDRESS

EMAIL

PHONE (H)

PHONE (W)

FAX

CELL/PAGER

NAME

ADDRESS

EMAIL

PHONE (H)

PHONE (W)

FAX

CELL/PAGER

NAME

ADDRESS

EMAIL

PHONE (H)

PHONE (W)

FAX

CELL/PAGER

NAME

ADDRESS

EMAIL

PHONE (H)

PHONE (W)

FAX

CELL/PAGER

Symmetry Watercolor 107
7⅞ x 7⅞ in., 1960

Symmetry Watercolor 98
7⅞ x 7⅞ in., 1955

NAME	PHONE (H)
ADDRESS	PHONE (W)
	FAX
EMAIL	CELL/PAGER

NAME	PHONE (H)
ADDRESS	PHONE (W)
	FAX
EMAIL	CELL/PAGER

NAME	PHONE (H)
ADDRESS	PHONE (W)
	FAX
EMAIL	CELL/PAGER

NAME	PHONE (H)
ADDRESS	PHONE (W)
	FAX
EMAIL	CELL/PAGER

NAME	PHONE (H)
ADDRESS	PHONE (W)
	FAX
EMAIL	CELL/PAGER

NAME	PHONE (H)
ADDRESS	PHONE (W)
	FAX
EMAIL	CELL/PAGER

NAME

ADDRESS

EMAIL

PHONE (H)

PHONE (W)

FAX

CELL/PAGER

NAME

ADDRESS

EMAIL

PHONE (H)

PHONE (W)

FAX

CELL/PAGER

NAME

ADDRESS

EMAIL

PHONE (H)

PHONE (W)

FAX

CELL/PAGER

NAME

ADDRESS

EMAIL

PHONE (H)

PHONE (W)

FAX

CELL/PAGER

NAME

ADDRESS

EMAIL

PHONE (H)

PHONE (W)

FAX

CELL/PAGER

NAME

ADDRESS

EMAIL

PHONE (H)

PHONE (W)

FAX

CELL/PAGER

NAME

ADDRESS

EMAIL

PHONE (H)

PHONE (W)

FAX

CELL/PAGER

NAME

ADDRESS

EMAIL

PHONE (H)

PHONE (W)

FAX

CELL/PAGER

NAME

ADDRESS

EMAIL

PHONE (H)

PHONE (W)

FAX

CELL/PAGER

NAME

ADDRESS

EMAIL

PHONE (H)

PHONE (W)

FAX

CELL/PAGER

NAME

ADDRESS

EMAIL

PHONE (H)

PHONE (W)

FAX

CELL/PAGER

NAME

ADDRESS

EMAIL

PHONE (H)

PHONE (W)

FAX

CELL/PAGER

NAME

ADDRESS

EMAIL

PHONE (H)

PHONE (W)

FAX

CELL/PAGER

NAME

ADDRESS

EMAIL

PHONE (H)

PHONE (W)

FAX

CELL/PAGER

NAME

ADDRESS

EMAIL

PHONE (H)

PHONE (W)

FAX

CELL/PAGER

NAME

ADDRESS

EMAIL

PHONE (H)

PHONE (W)

FAX

CELL/PAGER

NAME

ADDRESS

EMAIL

PHONE (H)

PHONE (W)

FAX

CELL/PAGER

NAME

ADDRESS

EMAIL

PHONE (H)

PHONE (W)

FAX

CELL/PAGER

0

Reptiles

Lithograph, 13⅛ x 15¼ in., 1943

Delft: (Interior) Nieuwe Kerk

Woodcut, 12⅜ x 8¼ in., 1939

NAME	PHONE (H)
ADDRESS	PHONE (W)
	FAX
EMAIL	CELL/PAGER

NAME	PHONE (H)
ADDRESS	PHONE (W)
	FAX
EMAIL	CELL/PAGER

NAME	PHONE (H)
ADDRESS	PHONE (W)
	FAX
EMAIL	CELL/PAGER

NAME	PHONE (H)
ADDRESS	PHONE (W)
	FAX
EMAIL	CELL/PAGER

NAME	PHONE (H)
ADDRESS	PHONE (W)
	FAX
EMAIL	CELL/PAGER

NAME	PHONE (H)
ADDRESS	PHONE (W)
	FAX
EMAIL	CELL/PAGER

NAME

ADDRESS

EMAIL

PHONE (H)

PHONE (W)

FAX

CELL/PAGER

NAME

ADDRESS

EMAIL

PHONE (H)

PHONE (W)

FAX

CELL/PAGER

NAME

ADDRESS

EMAIL

PHONE (H)

PHONE (W)

FAX

CELL/PAGER

NAME

ADDRESS

EMAIL

PHONE (H)

PHONE (W)

FAX

CELL/PAGER

NAME

ADDRESS

EMAIL

PHONE (H)

PHONE (W)

FAX

CELL/PAGER

NAME

ADDRESS

EMAIL

PHONE (H)

PHONE (W)

FAX

CELL/PAGER

NAME

ADDRESS

EMAIL

PHONE (H)

PHONE (W)

FAX

CELL/PAGER

NAME

ADDRESS

EMAIL

PHONE (H)

PHONE (W)

FAX

CELL/PAGER

NAME

ADDRESS

EMAIL

PHONE (H)

PHONE (W)

FAX

CELL/PAGER

NAME

ADDRESS

EMAIL

PHONE (H)

PHONE (W)

FAX

CELL/PAGER

NAME

ADDRESS

EMAIL

PHONE (H)

PHONE (W)

FAX

CELL/PAGER

NAME

ADDRESS

EMAIL

PHONE (H)

PHONE (W)

FAX

CELL/PAGER

NAME

ADDRESS

EMAIL

PHONE (H)

PHONE (W)

FAX

CELL/PAGER

NAME

ADDRESS

EMAIL

PHONE (H)

PHONE (W)

FAX

CELL/PAGER

NAME

ADDRESS

EMAIL

PHONE (H)

PHONE (W)

FAX

CELL/PAGER

NAME

ADDRESS

EMAIL

PHONE (H)

PHONE (W)

FAX

CELL/PAGER

NAME

ADDRESS

EMAIL

PHONE (H)

PHONE (W)

FAX

CELL/PAGER

NAME

ADDRESS

EMAIL

PHONE (H)

PHONE (W)

FAX

CELL/PAGER

NAME

ADDRESS

EMAIL

PHONE (H)

PHONE (W)

FAX

CELL/PAGER

Still Life with Spherical Mirror

Lithograph, 11¼ x 12⅞ in., 1934

P

Up and Down

Lithograph, 19¾ x 8⅛ in., 1947

NAME	PHONE (H)
ADDRESS	PHONE (W)
	FAX
EMAIL	CELL/PAGER

NAME	PHONE (H)
ADDRESS	PHONE (W)
	FAX
EMAIL	CELL/PAGER

NAME	PHONE (H)
ADDRESS	PHONE (W)
	FAX
EMAIL	CELL/PAGER

NAME	PHONE (H)
ADDRESS	PHONE (W)
	FAX
EMAIL	CELL/PAGER

NAME	PHONE (H)
ADDRESS	PHONE (W)
	FAX
EMAIL	CELL/PAGER

NAME	PHONE (H)
ADDRESS	PHONE (W)
	FAX
EMAIL	CELL/PAGER

NAME	PHONE (H)
ADDRESS	PHONE (W)
	FAX
EMAIL	CELL/PAGER

NAME	PHONE (H)
ADDRESS	PHONE (W)
	FAX
EMAIL	CELL/PAGER

NAME	PHONE (H)
ADDRESS	PHONE (W)
	FAX
EMAIL	CELL/PAGER

NAME	PHONE (H)
ADDRESS	PHONE (W)
	FAX
EMAIL	CELL/PAGER

NAME	PHONE (H)
ADDRESS	PHONE (W)
	FAX
EMAIL	CELL/PAGER

NAME	PHONE (H)
ADDRESS	PHONE (W)
	FAX
EMAIL	CELL/PAGER

NAME

PHONE (H)

ADDRESS

PHONE (W)

FAX

EMAIL

CELL/PAGER

NAME

PHONE (H)

ADDRESS

PHONE (W)

FAX

EMAIL

CELL/PAGER

NAME

PHONE (H)

ADDRESS

PHONE (W)

FAX

EMAIL

CELL/PAGER

NAME

PHONE (H)

ADDRESS

PHONE (W)

FAX

EMAIL

CELL/PAGER

NAME

PHONE (H)

ADDRESS

PHONE (W)

FAX

EMAIL

CELL/PAGER

NAME

PHONE (H)

ADDRESS

PHONE (W)

FAX

EMAIL

CELL/PAGER

NAME

ADDRESS

EMAIL

PHONE (H)

PHONE (W)

FAX

CELL/PAGER

NAME

ADDRESS

EMAIL

PHONE (H)

PHONE (W)

FAX

CELL/PAGER

NAME

ADDRESS

EMAIL

PHONE (H)

PHONE (W)

FAX

CELL/PAGER

NAME

ADDRESS

EMAIL

PHONE (H)

PHONE (W)

FAX

CELL/PAGER

NAME

ADDRESS

EMAIL

PHONE (H)

PHONE (W)

FAX

CELL/PAGER

NAME

ADDRESS

EMAIL

PHONE (H)

PHONE (W)

FAX

CELL/PAGER

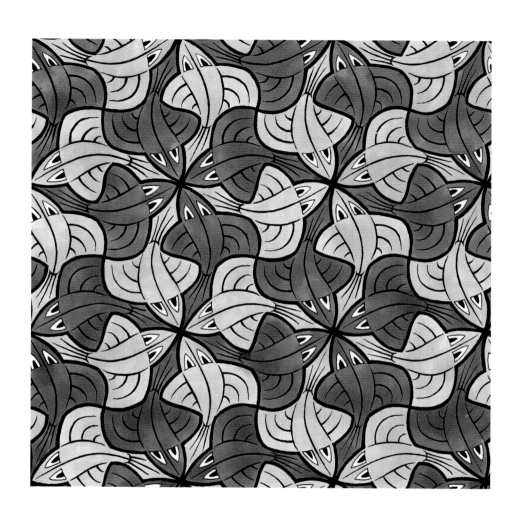

QR

Symmetry Watercolor 119
9⅝ x 9⅝ in., 1964

QR

Still Life and Street

Woodcut, 19³/₁₆ x 19¼ in., 1937

NAME

ADDRESS

EMAIL

PHONE (H)

PHONE (W)

FAX

CELL/PAGER

NAME

ADDRESS

EMAIL

PHONE (H)

PHONE (W)

FAX

CELL/PAGER

NAME

ADDRESS

EMAIL

PHONE (H)

PHONE (W)

FAX

CELL/PAGER

NAME

ADDRESS

EMAIL

PHONE (H)

PHONE (W)

FAX

CELL/PAGER

NAME

ADDRESS

EMAIL

PHONE (H)

PHONE (W)

FAX

CELL/PAGER

NAME

ADDRESS

EMAIL

PHONE (H)

PHONE (W)

FAX

CELL/PAGER

NAME

PHONE (H)

ADDRESS

PHONE (W)

FAX

EMAIL

CELL/PAGER

NAME

PHONE (H)

ADDRESS

PHONE (W)

FAX

EMAIL

CELL/PAGER

NAME

PHONE (H)

ADDRESS

PHONE (W)

FAX

EMAIL

CELL/PAGER

NAME

PHONE (H)

ADDRESS

PHONE (W)

FAX

EMAIL

CELL/PAGER

NAME

PHONE (H)

ADDRESS

PHONE (W)

FAX

EMAIL

CELL/PAGER

NAME

PHONE (H)

ADDRESS

PHONE (W)

FAX

EMAIL

CELL/PAGER

NAME	PHONE (H)
ADDRESS	PHONE (W)
	FAX
EMAIL	CELL/PAGER

NAME	PHONE (H)
ADDRESS	PHONE (W)
	FAX
EMAIL	CELL/PAGER

NAME	PHONE (H)
ADDRESS	PHONE (W)
	FAX
EMAIL	CELL/PAGER

NAME	PHONE (H)
ADDRESS	PHONE (W)
	FAX
EMAIL	CELL/PAGER

NAME	PHONE (H)
ADDRESS	PHONE (W)
	FAX
EMAIL	CELL/PAGER

NAME	PHONE (H)
ADDRESS	PHONE (W)
	FAX
EMAIL	CELL/PAGER

NAME

ADDRESS

EMAIL

PHONE (H)

PHONE (W)

FAX

CELL/PAGER

NAME

ADDRESS

EMAIL

PHONE (H)

PHONE (W)

FAX

CELL/PAGER

NAME

ADDRESS

EMAIL

PHONE (H)

PHONE (W)

FAX

CELL/PAGER

NAME

ADDRESS

EMAIL

PHONE (H)

PHONE (W)

FAX

CELL/PAGER

NAME

ADDRESS

EMAIL

PHONE (H)

PHONE (W)

FAX

CELL/PAGER

NAME

ADDRESS

EMAIL

PHONE (H)

PHONE (W)

FAX

CELL/PAGER

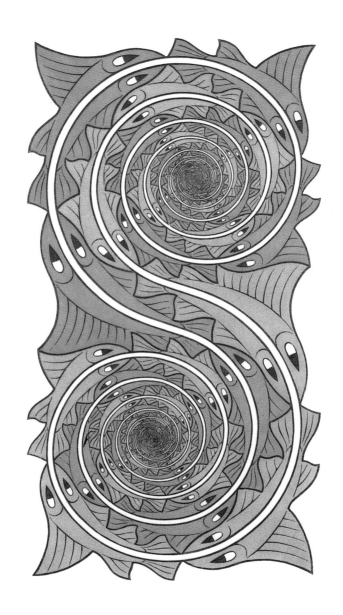

Whirlpools
Wood engraving and woodcut, 17¼ x 9¼ in., 1957

S

Symmetry Drawing 60

9¹⁵⁄₁₆ x 8½ in., 1942

NAME

ADDRESS

EMAIL

PHONE (H)

PHONE (W)

FAX

CELL/PAGER

NAME

ADDRESS

EMAIL

PHONE (H)

PHONE (W)

FAX

CELL/PAGER

NAME

ADDRESS

EMAIL

PHONE (H)

PHONE (W)

FAX

CELL/PAGER

NAME

ADDRESS

EMAIL

PHONE (H)

PHONE (W)

FAX

CELL/PAGER

NAME

ADDRESS

EMAIL

PHONE (H)

PHONE (W)

FAX

CELL/PAGER

NAME

ADDRESS

EMAIL

PHONE (H)

PHONE (W)

FAX

CELL/PAGER

NAME	PHONE (H)
ADDRESS	PHONE (W)
	FAX
EMAIL	CELL/PAGER

NAME	PHONE (H)
ADDRESS	PHONE (W)
	FAX
EMAIL	CELL/PAGER

NAME	PHONE (H)
ADDRESS	PHONE (W)
	FAX
EMAIL	CELL/PAGER

NAME	PHONE (H)
ADDRESS	PHONE (W)
	FAX
EMAIL	CELL/PAGER

NAME	PHONE (H)
ADDRESS	PHONE (W)
	FAX
EMAIL	CELL/PAGER

NAME	PHONE (H)
ADDRESS	PHONE (W)
	FAX
EMAIL	CELL/PAGER

NAME	PHONE (H)
ADDRESS	PHONE (W)
	FAX
EMAIL	CELL/PAGER

NAME	PHONE (H)
ADDRESS	PHONE (W)
	FAX
EMAIL	CELL/PAGER

NAME	PHONE (H)
ADDRESS	PHONE (W)
	FAX
EMAIL	CELL/PAGER

NAME	PHONE (H)
ADDRESS	PHONE (W)
	FAX
EMAIL	CELL/PAGER

NAME	PHONE (H)
ADDRESS	PHONE (W)
	FAX
EMAIL	CELL/PAGER

NAME	PHONE (H)
ADDRESS	PHONE (W)
	FAX
EMAIL	CELL/PAGER

NAME	PHONE (H)
ADDRESS	PHONE (W)
	FAX
EMAIL	CELL/PAGER

NAME	PHONE (H)
ADDRESS	PHONE (W)
	FAX
EMAIL	CELL/PAGER

NAME	PHONE (H)
ADDRESS	PHONE (W)
	FAX
EMAIL	CELL/PAGER

NAME	PHONE (H)
ADDRESS	PHONE (W)
	FAX
EMAIL	CELL/PAGER

NAME	PHONE (H)
ADDRESS	PHONE (W)
	FAX
EMAIL	CELL/PAGER

NAME	PHONE (H)
ADDRESS	PHONE (W)
	FAX
EMAIL	CELL/PAGER

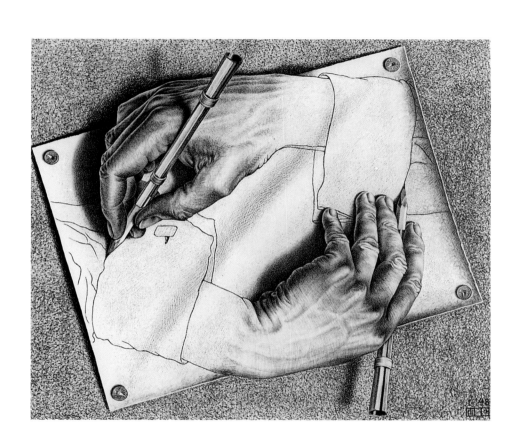

Drawing Hands
Lithograph, 11 x 13 in., 1948

T

Tower of Babel

Woodcut, 24½ x 15¼ in., 1928

NAME

ADDRESS

EMAIL

PHONE (H)

PHONE (W)

FAX

CELL/PAGER

NAME

ADDRESS

EMAIL

PHONE (H)

PHONE (W)

FAX

CELL/PAGER

NAME

ADDRESS

EMAIL

PHONE (H)

PHONE (W)

FAX

CELL/PAGER

NAME

ADDRESS

EMAIL

PHONE (H)

PHONE (W)

FAX

CELL/PAGER

NAME

ADDRESS

EMAIL

PHONE (H)

PHONE (W)

FAX

CELL/PAGER

NAME

ADDRESS

EMAIL

PHONE (H)

PHONE (W)

FAX

CELL/PAGER

NAME _____ PHONE (H) _____

ADDRESS _____ PHONE (W) _____

_____ FAX _____

EMAIL _____ CELL/PAGER _____

NAME _____ PHONE (H) _____

ADDRESS _____ PHONE (W) _____

_____ FAX _____

EMAIL _____ CELL/PAGER _____

NAME _____ PHONE (H) _____

ADDRESS _____ PHONE (W) _____

_____ FAX _____

EMAIL _____ CELL/PAGER _____

NAME _____ PHONE (H) _____

ADDRESS _____ PHONE (W) _____

_____ FAX _____

EMAIL _____ CELL/PAGER _____

NAME _____ PHONE (H) _____

ADDRESS _____ PHONE (W) _____

_____ FAX _____

EMAIL _____ CELL/PAGER _____

NAME _____ PHONE (H) _____

ADDRESS _____ PHONE (W) _____

_____ FAX _____

EMAIL _____ CELL/PAGER _____

NAME	PHONE (H)
ADDRESS	PHONE (W)
	FAX
EMAIL	CELL/PAGER

NAME	PHONE (H)
ADDRESS	PHONE (W)
	FAX
EMAIL	CELL/PAGER

NAME	PHONE (H)
ADDRESS	PHONE (W)
	FAX
EMAIL	CELL/PAGER

NAME	PHONE (H)
ADDRESS	PHONE (W)
	FAX
EMAIL	CELL/PAGER

NAME	PHONE (H)
ADDRESS	PHONE (W)
	FAX
EMAIL	CELL/PAGER

NAME	PHONE (H)
ADDRESS	PHONE (W)
	FAX
EMAIL	CELL/PAGER

NAME

ADDRESS

EMAIL

PHONE (H)

PHONE (W)

FAX

CELL/PAGER

NAME

ADDRESS

EMAIL

PHONE (H)

PHONE (W)

FAX

CELL/PAGER

NAME

ADDRESS

EMAIL

PHONE (H)

PHONE (W)

FAX

CELL/PAGER

NAME

ADDRESS

EMAIL

PHONE (H)

PHONE (W)

FAX

CELL/PAGER

NAME

ADDRESS

EMAIL

PHONE (H)

PHONE (W)

FAX

CELL/PAGER

NAME

ADDRESS

EMAIL

PHONE (H)

PHONE (W)

FAX

CELL/PAGER

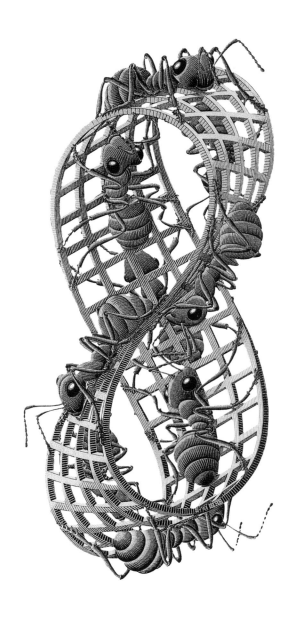

Möbius Strip II
Woodcut, 17⅞ x 8⅛ in., 1963

Delft: Roofs

Woodcut, 7¾ x 8 in., 1939

NAME _____ PHONE (H) _____

ADDRESS _____ PHONE (W) _____

_____ FAX _____

EMAIL _____ CELL/PAGER _____

NAME _____ PHONE (H) _____

ADDRESS _____ PHONE (W) _____

_____ FAX _____

EMAIL _____ CELL/PAGER _____

NAME _____ PHONE (H) _____

ADDRESS _____ PHONE (W) _____

_____ FAX _____

EMAIL _____ CELL/PAGER _____

NAME _____ PHONE (H) _____

ADDRESS _____ PHONE (W) _____

_____ FAX _____

EMAIL _____ CELL/PAGER _____

NAME _____ PHONE (H) _____

ADDRESS _____ PHONE (W) _____

_____ FAX _____

EMAIL _____ CELL/PAGER _____

NAME _____ PHONE (H) _____

ADDRESS _____ PHONE (W) _____

_____ FAX _____

EMAIL _____ CELL/PAGER _____

NAME

ADDRESS

EMAIL

PHONE (H)

PHONE (W)

FAX

CELL/PAGER

NAME

ADDRESS

EMAIL

PHONE (H)

PHONE (W)

FAX

CELL/PAGER

NAME

ADDRESS

EMAIL

PHONE (H)

PHONE (W)

FAX

CELL/PAGER

NAME

ADDRESS

EMAIL

PHONE (H)

PHONE (W)

FAX

CELL/PAGER

NAME

ADDRESS

EMAIL

PHONE (H)

PHONE (W)

FAX

CELL/PAGER

NAME

ADDRESS

EMAIL

PHONE (H)

PHONE (W)

FAX

CELL/PAGER

NAME

ADDRESS

EMAIL

PHONE (H)

PHONE (W)

FAX

CELL/PAGER

NAME

ADDRESS

EMAIL

PHONE (H)

PHONE (W)

FAX

CELL/PAGER

NAME

ADDRESS

EMAIL

PHONE (H)

PHONE (W)

FAX

CELL/PAGER

NAME

ADDRESS

EMAIL

PHONE (H)

PHONE (W)

FAX

CELL/PAGER

NAME

ADDRESS

EMAIL

PHONE (H)

PHONE (W)

FAX

CELL/PAGER

NAME

ADDRESS

EMAIL

PHONE (H)

PHONE (W)

FAX

CELL/PAGER

NAME

ADDRESS

EMAIL

PHONE (H)

PHONE (W)

FAX

CELL/PAGER

NAME

ADDRESS

EMAIL

PHONE (H)

PHONE (W)

FAX

CELL/PAGER

NAME

ADDRESS

EMAIL

PHONE (H)

PHONE (W)

FAX

CELL/PAGER

NAME

ADDRESS

EMAIL

PHONE (H)

PHONE (W)

FAX

CELL/PAGER

NAME

ADDRESS

EMAIL

PHONE (H)

PHONE (W)

FAX

CELL/PAGER

NAME

ADDRESS

EMAIL

PHONE (H)

PHONE (W)

FAX

CELL/PAGER

Symmetry Watercolor 116

7⅞ x 7⅞ in., 1963

W

Fish and Scales

Woodcut, 14⅞ x 14⅞ in., 1959

NAME

ADDRESS

EMAIL

PHONE (H)

PHONE (W)

FAX

CELL/PAGER

NAME

ADDRESS

EMAIL

PHONE (H)

PHONE (W)

FAX

CELL/PAGER

NAME

ADDRESS

EMAIL

PHONE (H)

PHONE (W)

FAX

CELL/PAGER

NAME

ADDRESS

EMAIL

PHONE (H)

PHONE (W)

FAX

CELL/PAGER

NAME

ADDRESS

EMAIL

PHONE (H)

PHONE (W)

FAX

CELL/PAGER

NAME

ADDRESS

EMAIL

PHONE (H)

PHONE (W)

FAX

CELL/PAGER

NAME

ADDRESS

EMAIL

PHONE (H)

PHONE (W)

FAX

CELL/PAGER

NAME

ADDRESS

EMAIL

PHONE (H)

PHONE (W)

FAX

CELL/PAGER

NAME

ADDRESS

EMAIL

PHONE (H)

PHONE (W)

FAX

CELL/PAGER

NAME

ADDRESS

EMAIL

PHONE (H)

PHONE (W)

FAX

CELL/PAGER

NAME

ADDRESS

EMAIL

PHONE (H)

PHONE (W)

FAX

CELL/PAGER

NAME

ADDRESS

EMAIL

PHONE (H)

PHONE (W)

FAX

CELL/PAGER

NAME

PHONE (H)

ADDRESS

PHONE (W)

FAX

EMAIL

CELL/PAGER

NAME

PHONE (H)

ADDRESS

PHONE (W)

FAX

EMAIL

CELL/PAGER

NAME

PHONE (H)

ADDRESS

PHONE (W)

FAX

EMAIL

CELL/PAGER

NAME

PHONE (H)

ADDRESS

PHONE (W)

FAX

EMAIL

CELL/PAGER

NAME

PHONE (H)

ADDRESS

PHONE (W)

FAX

EMAIL

CELL/PAGER

NAME

PHONE (H)

ADDRESS

PHONE (W)

FAX

EMAIL

CELL/PAGER

NAME	PHONE (H)
ADDRESS	PHONE (W)
	FAX
EMAIL	CELL/PAGER

NAME	PHONE (H)
ADDRESS	PHONE (W)
	FAX
EMAIL	CELL/PAGER

NAME	PHONE (H)
ADDRESS	PHONE (W)
	FAX
EMAIL	CELL/PAGER

NAME	PHONE (H)
ADDRESS	PHONE (W)
	FAX
EMAIL	CELL/PAGER

NAME	PHONE (H)
ADDRESS	PHONE (W)
	FAX
EMAIL	CELL/PAGER

NAME	PHONE (H)
ADDRESS	PHONE (W)
	FAX
EMAIL	CELL/PAGER

Castrovalva

Lithograph, 16⅝ x 12⅛ in., 1930

Symmetry Watercolor 106
7⅞ x 7⅞ in., 1959

NAME _____ PHONE (H) _____

ADDRESS _____ PHONE (W) _____

_____ FAX _____

EMAIL _____ CELL/PAGER _____

NAME _____ PHONE (H) _____

ADDRESS _____ PHONE (W) _____

_____ FAX _____

EMAIL _____ CELL/PAGER _____

NAME _____ PHONE (H) _____

ADDRESS _____ PHONE (W) _____

_____ FAX _____

EMAIL _____ CELL/PAGER _____

NAME _____ PHONE (H) _____

ADDRESS _____ PHONE (W) _____

_____ FAX _____

EMAIL _____ CELL/PAGER _____

NAME _____ PHONE (H) _____

ADDRESS _____ PHONE (W) _____

_____ FAX _____

EMAIL _____ CELL/PAGER _____

NAME _____ PHONE (H) _____

ADDRESS _____ PHONE (W) _____

_____ FAX _____

EMAIL _____ CELL/PAGER _____

NAME

PHONE (H)

ADDRESS

PHONE (W)

FAX

EMAIL

CELL/PAGER

NAME

PHONE (H)

ADDRESS

PHONE (W)

FAX

EMAIL

CELL/PAGER

NAME

PHONE (H)

ADDRESS

PHONE (W)

FAX

EMAIL

CELL/PAGER

NAME

PHONE (H)

ADDRESS

PHONE (W)

FAX

EMAIL

CELL/PAGER

NAME

PHONE (H)

ADDRESS

PHONE (W)

FAX

EMAIL

CELL/PAGER

NAME

PHONE (H)

ADDRESS

PHONE (W)

FAX

EMAIL

CELL/PAGER

NAME

ADDRESS

EMAIL

PHONE (H)

PHONE (W)

FAX

CELL/PAGER

NAME

ADDRESS

EMAIL

PHONE (H)

PHONE (W)

FAX

CELL/PAGER

NAME

ADDRESS

EMAIL

PHONE (H)

PHONE (W)

FAX

CELL/PAGER

NAME

ADDRESS

EMAIL

PHONE (H)

PHONE (W)

FAX

CELL/PAGER

NAME

ADDRESS

EMAIL

PHONE (H)

PHONE (W)

FAX

CELL/PAGER

NAME

ADDRESS

EMAIL

PHONE (H)

PHONE (W)

FAX

CELL/PAGER

NAME _____

PHONE (H) _____

ADDRESS _____

PHONE (W) _____

_____

FAX _____

EMAIL _____

CELL/PAGER _____

NAME _____

PHONE (H) _____

ADDRESS _____

PHONE (W) _____

_____

FAX _____

EMAIL _____

CELL/PAGER _____

NAME _____

PHONE (H) _____

ADDRESS _____

PHONE (W) _____

_____

FAX _____

EMAIL _____

CELL/PAGER _____

NAME _____

PHONE (H) _____

ADDRESS _____

PHONE (W) _____

_____

FAX _____

EMAIL _____

CELL/PAGER _____

NAME _____

PHONE (H) _____

ADDRESS _____

PHONE (W) _____

_____

FAX _____

EMAIL _____

CELL/PAGER _____

NAME _____

PHONE (H) _____

ADDRESS _____

PHONE (W) _____

_____

FAX _____

EMAIL _____

CELL/PAGER _____